Bitty Twins
Learn to Share

Written by Jennifer Hirsch
Illustrated by Stephanie Roth

Do you have a sibling? If you do,
you probably have one who's older than you
or one who's younger. That's because
most siblings are not twins, like us.

Even though we're sister and brother,
we were together inside our mother,
and we were born at the same time.

That's quite rare! It means that I'm
only one minute older than he,
and he's just one minute younger than me.

Since we're twins, we share a lot.

We like to share our best robot,
the one that can walk and talk and blink.

We share our stove and built-in sink
where we pretend to wash the dishes.

We also share our sharks and fishes.

We share dolls and trucks and blocks.
Sometimes we even share our socks!

But we don't always want to share.
For instance, when I'm in my chair,
about to eat some mac and cheese—
and without even saying "please,"

my brother takes some macaroni
or a piece of my baloney.
Then I tell him, loud and clear,
"This is *my* lunch—do you hear?"

When we're playing
in the back,
and I'm building
a railroad track,
sometimes my sister
tries to take
some pieces so that
she can make . . .

a fence for her farm!
Can you believe it?

This makes a perfect fence. I need it!

No! This is a railroad track,
and it's all mine. Now give it back!

All right, you two—I don't care
whose toy this is. You have to share.

Let's build the train track so it goes
past the farm. And with the hose

and a pile of rocks, we'll make
a waterfall and a real lake!

See? Playing is a lot more fun
when you share it with someone.

It's hard at first,
but that's okay.

We try to share
whenever we play.

Especially on our special day,

which we *have* to share—

our twin birthday!

Dear Parents . . .

Sharing is not something young children are born knowing how to do. They learn how to share by imitating others or following your instructions. Once they discover the rewards of sharing, it begins to come naturally. Until then, you can help them learn to be good sharers.

Is She Ready?

Before they turn three, most children cannot "put themselves in someone else's shoes" and, therefore, don't understand the point of sharing. A two-year-old's natural instinct is to keep a grip on her possessions and to grab what she wants. If your child does this, it doesn't mean she's selfish or a bully; it just means she's young. At this age, the best way to encourage group play is by having plenty of toys to go around.

When another toddler wants a turn with your child's toy, try offering your child another toy in exchange. Or limit group play to things you have lots of, such as blocks, cars, stuffed animals, or the like.

Different Ways of Sharing

Sometimes sharing means taking turns; other times it means playing together with the same toy. Mastering either type of sharing is a developmental milestone to be praised. Tell your little one, "I really like the way you threw the ball to Shawn!"

Here are some other positive ways to introduce the concept of sharing:

• **Make it a game.** Say in a sing-song voice, "First Sarah drives the train, then Megan takes a turn . . . and now it's Sarah's turn again!"

• **Use a timer.** Each child gets the toy for two minutes. When the timer goes off, it's time to switch. Hearing the timer go off is so exciting that your little ones may actually look forward to it!

• **Help them anticipate.** Children become so engrossed in play that being told it's time to give up a toy can come as a shock. Tell them, "Let's sing 'Row, Row, Row Your Boat' three times, and when we're done, it will be Max's turn."

• **Be a role model.** When your child plays with something of yours, point it out: "Hey, I'm sharing my slippers with you!" Then suggest that she find something of hers to share with you. She'll feel honored to share with her parent, and it will be great practice for sharing with her friends.